the old barn

by Carol and Donald Carrick

The Bobbs-Merrill Company, Inc.
A Subsidiary of Howard W. Sams & Co., Inc.
Publishers • Indianapolis • Kansas City • New York

for Lucien

C 316 a

Far away, where houses have no neighbors,
stands the old barn...
old as your grandfather's grandfather.

snow after snow
leans for
months

against it.

When the drifts melt,
the bottom of the barn appears.

Now Mouse can use

his private door.

On early summer mornings

the barn is lost in mist...

washed
in dew

and dried by the rising sun.

Flower fields soak up

the golden light.

Bugs are hopping, humming, whirring, watching,

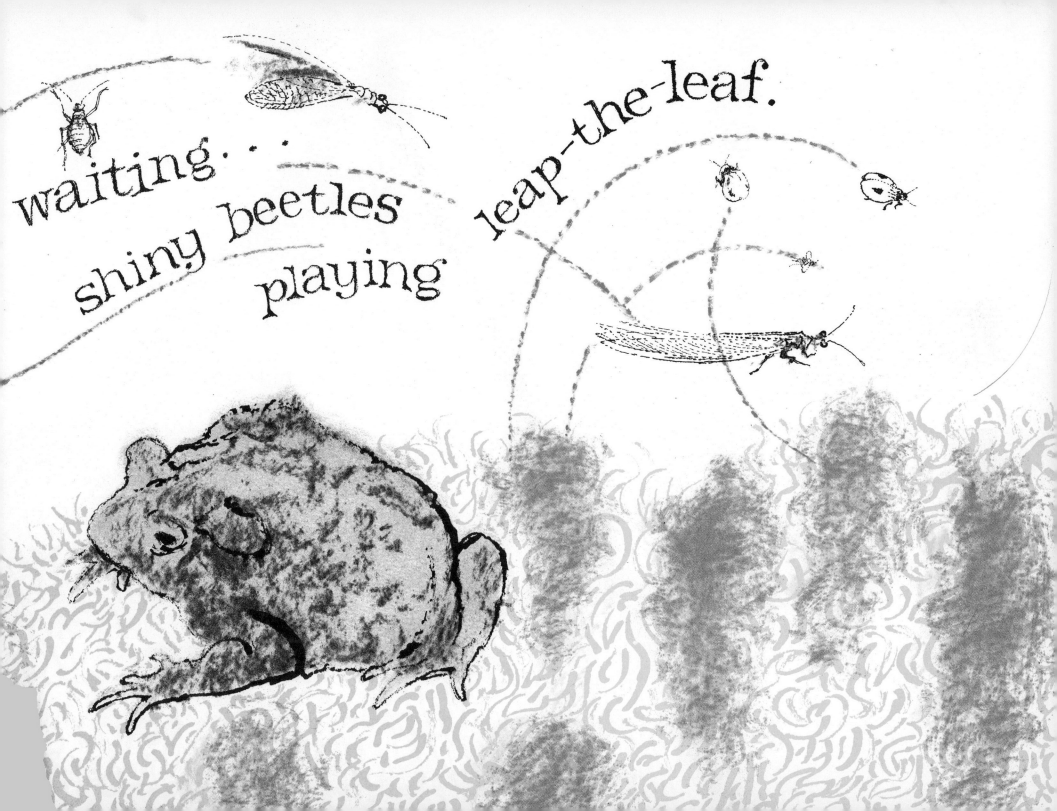

waiting . . .
shiny beetles
playing
leap-the-leaf.

Up above the graceful swallows

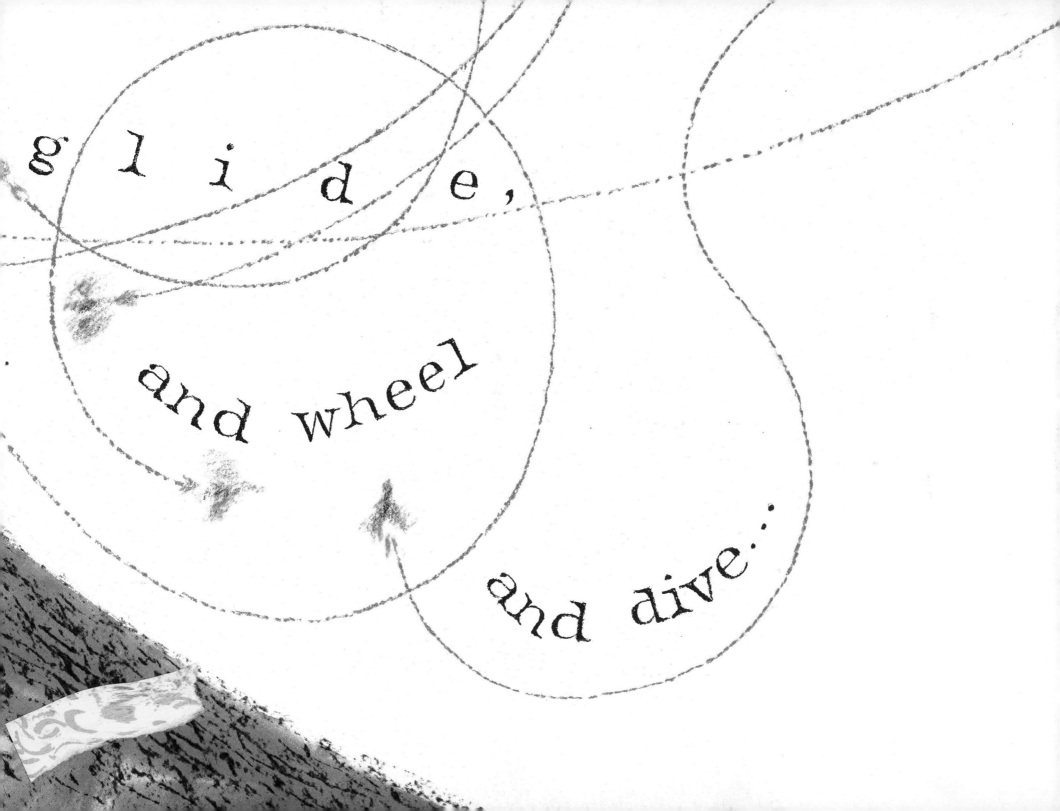

snatching
fat flies

to still
their babies'
clamoring.

Inside
all is
dusty, dark
and
still...

when
sudden

summer storms
splash
on the roof,
spilling
from the eaves
in silver sheets.

But sleepers
in the loft
stay
snug and dry

. . . . in nooks

and nests   and rafters,

while from below comes the
sound of gnawing
on the soft old wood.

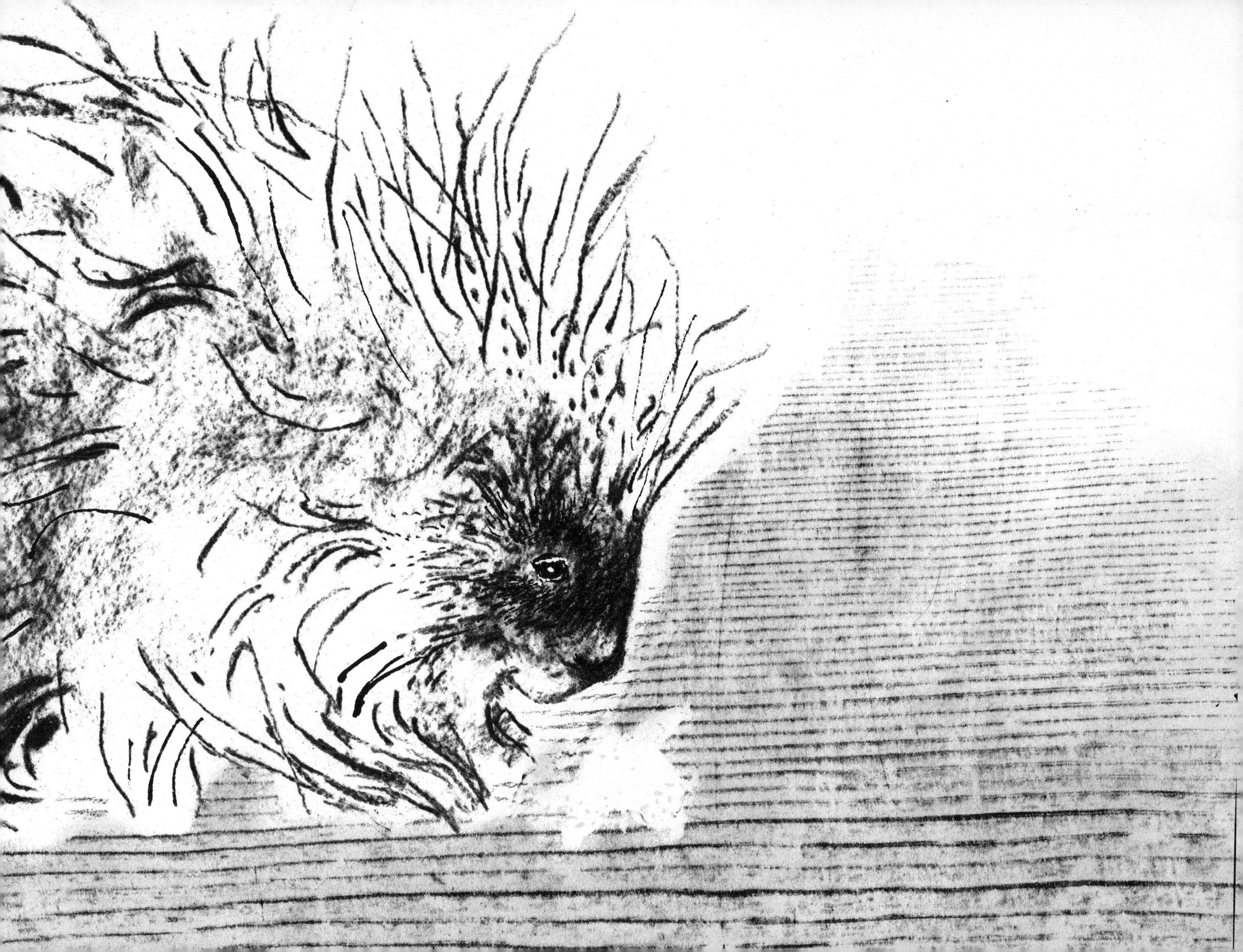

The storm moves on,
uncovering the stars,

as Owl awakes
to hunt for mice.

And from the barn,
on soundless wings,
night creatures come and go.